GW01003495

Football
Stories
that
Really Happened

Other books in this series…

Space Stories that Really Happened

by Andrew Donkin

Animal Stories that Really Happened

by Pat Posner

Horse Stories that Really Happened

by Diana Kimpton

Coming soon…

Dinosaur Stories that Really Happened

by Andrew Donkin

Football
Stories
that
Really Happened

Alan MacDonald

Illustrated by Paul Dainton

Scholastic Children's Books,
Commonwealth House, 1-19 New Oxford Street,
London WC1A 1NU, UK

A division of Scholastic Ltd
London ~ New York ~ Toronto ~ Sydney ~ Auckland
Mexico City ~ New Delhi ~ Hong Kong

Published in the UK by Scholastic Ltd, 2000

Text copyright © Alan MacDonald, 2000
Illustrations copyright © Paul Dainton, 2000

ISBN 0 439 01269 4

All rights reserved
Typeset by Falcon Oast Graphic Art Ltd.
Printed and bound by The Bath Press, Bath

2 4 6 8 10 9 7 5 3 1

The right of Alan MacDonald and Paul Dainton to be identified
as the author and illustrator of this work respectively has been
asserted by them in accordance with the Copyright, Designs and
Patents Act, 1988.

This book is sold subject to the condition that it shall not, by way of
trade or otherwise be lent, resold, hired out, or otherwise circulated
without the publisher's prior consent in any form of binding or cover
other than that in which it is published and without a similar
condition, including this condition, being imposed
on a subsequent purchaser.

Contents

The Wizard of Dribble   7

Supersub   29

Pelé, King of the Street   51

Pickles Saves the World Cup   72

The Hungarian Heroes   95

Football Crazy Mum   118

Before you begin…

Who wants to be a footballer? When I was at school that was everybody's dream – including mine!

The marvellous thing about football is that every season dreams come true. In this book I've written about some of the greatest moments in football history. There are stories about football-mad fans, wing-play wizards, barefoot Brazilians and even a dog who became a World Cup hero.

Sometimes I've had to imagine characters or conversations to fill in the missing details, but all the stories in this book are true.

Who wants to play for their country, score at Wembley or win the World Cup? Well … there's nothing to stop us dreaming, is there?

Alan MacDonald

The Wizard of Dribble

Wembley Stadium, London, 1953

We were going to the FA Cup Final, Dad and me. Our team, Blackpool, had reached the final and were playing at Wembley. Not only that, but on the right wing we had Stanley Matthews – the Wizard of Dribble. I knew all about "our Stan" from my dad. "He's the greatest player you'll ever see," Dad said. With the ball at his feet, Stan was a magician.

He had played for England and been voted Footballer of the Year. There was only one thing Stan had never done. He'd never climbed the long staircase at Wembley to receive an FA Cup winner's medal. This was the third time Stan had been to Wembley in six years. Twice before Blackpool had reached the Cup Final and twice he'd walked off the pitch at the final whistle a loser.

This would be the great man's last chance. At 38 years old, he was past the age when most footballers hung up their boots for good. But Stan still had the magic in his feet. Surely this time the Wizard of Dribble would win it for Blackpool? Dad was certain of it. Never mind that we were playing mighty Bolton Wanderers. Never mind that Bolton had Nat Lofthouse – an England centre forward with a shot like a bullet. It was Stan's year and we were going to watch him.

I knew Stanley Matthews' story off by heart. He was the son of a boxer, Jack Matthews. Jack was nicknamed the Fighting Barber because he cut people's hair when he wasn't knocking them out in the ring. Jack wanted his sons to be fit like him. At six o'clock in the morning he dragged Stan and his brothers out of bed to do deep-breathing exercises and lift heavy weights. It never gave young Stan a body rippling with muscles. On a football pitch he looked skinny and bow-legged. Yet Stan was lightning-fast over a short sprint. He even designed his own extra-light football boots to give him that extra yard of pace to get past defenders. Like all the best conjurers he had his own book of tricks. When the ball was passed to Stan you never knew what he would do. Sometimes he shuffled forward – prodding the ball with little touches, daring the defender to try and get it. The defender would back off, watching the ball, already caught hopelessly in the spell. Stan would lean to the left, his feet spread wide apart.

"Watch me, watch me, I'm going left," his body would say. Sooner or later, the defender would *have* to move left. In that second he was lost. Stan whipped the ball back on his boot and sped off to the right. As he raced for the goal-line, the full-back was left marking thin air. It was like trying to catch the Invisible Man.

"They'll never stop Stan," said my dad, as we arrived at Wembley. "He'll tie them in knots. He'll make them wish they'd never turned up. The Cup's as good as won."

I hoped he was right. I felt a tingle of excitement as the turnstiles clicked and we entered the great stadium. Wembley – the most famous pitch in the world. Today 100,000 fans would be packed inside, roaring at the tops of their voices. Even the Queen was coming. Earlier that year our family had crowded round my uncle's black and white television to watch the young Queen Elizabeth crowned. Today I was going to see her for myself. She'd shake the hand of the great Stanley Matthews as she handed him his winner's medal. That was how it would end, Dad was certain. Blackpool couldn't lose three times in a row, could they?

All around us fans were wearing Blackpool colours – orange and white. The match kicked off to a great roar from the crowd.

"Come on, Blackpool. Come

on, Stan!" shouted my Dad. He lifted me on to his shoulders so that I could see above the heads of the crowd. I could see the black and white scarves of the Bolton fans at the other end. I bet they wished  they had the Wizard of Dribble on their side. I searched for him on the right touch-line. There he was, his shoulders hunched, his pale face topped by thinning hair. I had to admit he didn't look much like a wizard at all.

From the start something was wrong with Blackpool. Maybe they were remembering how they'd come to Wembley twice before and lost. The great stadium seemed to sap their confidence. Two minutes after the kick-off Bolton's big centre-forward, Nat Lofthouse, got the ball.

"Tackle 'im," shouted my Dad. "Get into 'im!"

But Blackpool's defenders were like statues. Lofthouse shot from about twenty yards out. It wasn't one of his bullets. The shot looked almost half-hearted, but our goalkeeper, Farm, dived too late. The ball bounced once and nestled in the corner of

the net. Farm held his head in horror. The game had only just started and Blackpool were one goal down!

"What was he doing?" Dad moaned to his pals. "My missus could have stopped that shot!"

I watched Blackpool kick off. There was

still plenty of time to play. Stan would teach Bolton a thing or two. But instead of Stan, it was the towering Lofthouse who had the game by the scruff of the neck. He was running at Blackpool's defence again and they looked bewildered. This time he hit the shot with all his power. The ball flew like a torpedo towards Blackpool's goal.

Farm, the goalkeeper, stood rooted to the spot. The Bolton fans were already jumping in the air, saluting the goal, when the ball smacked loudly against a post and rebounded out.

"Ooooh!" went the crowd, unable to believe Blackpool's luck. Farm looked as if he wished he could catch the next train home. Shots were raining in on his goal from all sides.

The game flowed fast. At the other end Blackpool got a goal back, but our hopes weren't raised for long. Soon Farm had let in another soft shot. Bolton went in at half-time 2-1 ahead and we all knew that the score could have been much worse. Dad lifted me down off his aching shoulders.

"What's wrong with them?" I asked.

He shook his head in despair. "I don't know, son. They're just not playing. We're letting that Lofthouse do what he likes."

"But what about Stan?" I asked.

Dad spread his hands. "He just hasn't had the ball. They're not getting it to him."

"Can't he do something?" I moaned. "He's the best player on the pitch. You said so."

Dad tried to explain that even a genius like Stan needed the rest of the team. A winger has to be fed the ball so that he can run at the defence and get in a cross. That was Stan's game – to beat defenders and cross the ball with deadly accuracy for someone else to score. But unless his team gave him the ball, he was powerless.

I nodded miserably but I wasn't convinced. If Stan was the greatest footballer ever born why didn't he win the game for us? He could just waltz round the Bolton team and score himself. Surely the Wizard of Dribble could do it if he tried? For weeks and weeks I'd been looking forward to this final. Now it was turning out all wrong.

Dad hoisted me back on to his shoulders as the second half kicked off. Blackpool were kicking towards the goal in front of us. Soon after the start a player got injured.

"Who's down? It's not Stan, is it?" I asked anxiously.

It was a Bolton player called Bell. When he got to his feet, he could only hobble around, limping badly. The crowd clapped him for staying on even though he could hardly run at all. (In those days there were no substitutes. If a player went off, the team had to play on with ten players.)

"They're down to ten men," Dad called up to me. "You watch, we'll be all over them like a rash now!"

How wrong can you be? Ten minutes later a high cross swung into Blackpool's penalty area. One player in white soared high above everybody else to head it home. Amazingly the scorer was Bell, who had looked out of the game moments before. Bolton were leading 3-1. It looked as if Blackpool's hopes of finally lifting the Cup were dead and buried.

As the Blackpool team trudged back to the halfway line, I looked for Stan. He hadn't done anything out of the ordinary so far. He was standing with his hands on his hips. He walked over and had a quiet word with our centre forward, Stan

 Mortenson. His face gave nothing away. But I thought that there was something determined about him as he stalked off back to find his position on the wing.

With Bolton down to ten fit men, Blackpool started to drag themselves back into the game. It was now a desperate race against time. Could they score two goals before the referee blew his whistle? I watched the clock tick round as Bolton defended grimly. There were only twenty minutes left to play. It looked as if Blackpool had left it too late. Stan was never going to get his hands on that cup winner's medal now.

"Come on Stan, show 'em Stan!" shouted my dad.

Stan had the ball on the right. He did his favourite trick. He leaned one way then whipped the ball back to go the other way. He was past one defender. Another rushed across to tackle him. Stan let him come, steaming in like an express train. At the last second, he stepped neatly inside him and sped away with the ball. He left a trail of Bolton defenders behind as he darted this way and that.

Then he crossed the ball into the area. It hung in the air, tempting the goalkeeper to come out. But Mortenson got there first to head the ball into the empty net. Goal!

Bolton 3 – Blackpool 2.

Now the Bolton defence froze every time Stan had the ball. He ran at them, stopping, starting, corkscrewing round and speeding off the other way. This was what

I'd come to see − the Wizard of Dribble casting his spell. Yet the minutes were ticking away and Blackpool couldn't get the vital equalizer.

There were three minutes left when Blackpool got a free-kick outside the penalty area. Every Bolton player came back to make a wall of white shirts across the goal.

Stan Mortenson took the kick for Blackpool. His shot flew like an arrow past the wall and into the back of the net. The ground erupted with a deafening noise. Blackpool were level! It was 3-3.

With less than a minute left the game seemed to be heading for extra time. But Stanley Matthews wasn't finished. He had the ball just inside the Bolton half and began another of those mazy runs. One defender lunged for a tackle and was left floundering on the grass. Stan went past the helpless full-back with a burst of speed, heading straight for the goal-line.

Bolton's centre-half was drawn across to cut out the danger. This was exactly what Stan wanted. He ran the ball straight at the defender as if he meant to pass through him like a ghost. At the last second he swerved outside. The cross came over hard and low. I let out a groan. Stan had put it too far behind Mortenson. But he wasn't aiming for him. He'd picked out Blackpool's left-winger, Perry, unmarked on the penalty  spot. Joyfully Perry swept the ball into the net for the winner. Dad was jumping up and down so much I nearly fell off his shoulders. Blackpool had done it. They'd come back from 3–1 down to win 4–3 in the last 20 minutes. When the whistle finally went we cheered

like mad, and Stan was carried round
Wembley on the shoulders of his team-mates.

The Wizard of Dribble hadn't let us
down. He'd saved his magic right till the
end. The win had been conjured from
nowhere, like a rabbit from a hat. That day
Stan finally got his winner's medal from
the Queen. And I went home on the train
to Blackpool, singing all the way.

Did you know…?

The FA Cup

1. The first ever Football Association (FA) Cup was won by a team called the Wanderers in 1872. They beat the Royal Engineers 1-0, and were watched by 2,000 people at the Oval ground in London, where cricket matches are now played.

2. Manchester United hold the record for winning the FA Cup. The Red Devils have lifted the cup ten times between 1909 and 1999. The Scottish FA Cup has been won by Celtic a record 30 times.

3. One of the biggest heroes in FA Cup history is a white horse called Billy. Together with his rider, Constable Scorey, this brave horse cleared thousands of people off the Wembley pitch at the FA Cup Final in 1923.

4. The youngest player to score in an FA Cup Final was Norman Whiteside. He was just 18 years old when he scored for Manchester United in the replay of the 1983 final against Brighton. Two years later he scored the only and winning goal for United in the Final against Everton. At the time his weekly wage was £350. Today some Manchester United players earn more than £20,000 a week!

5. The FA Cup is a world famous knock-out competition. But some teams have stubbornly refused to be knocked out! The record for the most replayed matches goes to Oxford United and Alvechurch. In their 1971 fourth round match they played a staggering six games before Alvechurch eventually won 1-0.

Supersub

The Island of Réunion, 1990

Roger Milla waved his arms in the air.
"No, no, no! Stop the game! Emile, what
are you doing?"

Seventeen-year-old Emile stood with
his hands on his hips in the centre circle.
He stared at his team coach, bemused.
"Nothing," he said. "We'd lost the ball."

Milla shook his head. "Never, never stop
playing. You are part of the team. Always

look for the ball. As a striker you never know when your chance will come."

The young player listened respectfully, nodding his head. To the St Pierre de la Réunion team, their coach was a footballing legend. Everyone in Africa had heard of Roger Milla. In his long career he'd won more honours than most players ever dream of.

In 1977 he'd been voted African Footballer of the Year. He had played in three championship finals in France and scored many memorable goals for the Cameroon national side. Now, at 38 years old, Milla had decided his international days were over. For a while he'd run a company selling sports shirts, but football remained his first love, so when the call came from the tiny island of Réunion to coach St Pierre, Milla had jumped at the chance. St Pierre were neither famous nor highly successful, but Milla didn't mind. In his career he'd had his fair share of fame and glory. It was all in the past now – or so he thought.

As Milla was coaching his team, a stranger appeared on the touchline and stood watching. His pale solemn face looked as if it was carved out of granite. Milla turned and recognized him. It was Valeri Nepomniachi, the Russian who was coach to the Cameroon national team. What did he want? Milla wondered. Re-starting the game he went over to find out.

After exchanging greetings, Valeri got straight to the point. "I've got a proposal for you. I want you to come and play in the

World Cup in Italy."

Milla threw back his head and laughed. "Is this a joke?"

"I never joke about football," said Valeri seriously.

"You know I've retired, Valeri. Anyway I'm 38! I'm too old to play in the World Cup."

"I don't think so," replied the Russian. "And neither do others. I've had a special request to take you along – from Paul Biya himself. "

"The President?" Milla's face broke into one of his wide, beaming smiles. "The President asked for me personally?"

Valeri nodded. An hour later Roger Milla was packing his bags to leave.

Cameroon lies in central Africa. With 12 million people, it has around a quarter the population of England. But while England has 41,000 registered football coaches to choose from, Cameroon has only 15 in the whole country! In 1990 African sides were seen as the minnows of world football. Cameroon, the Lions of Africa, were about to change all that.

The Lions had been to the World Cup before but had never managed to get past the first round. In 1990 few experts expected them to fare any better in Italy. It didn't help that Cameroon's very first game of the tournament was against mighty

Argentina. Argentina were the reigning World Cup champions. Not only that but they also had Diego Maradona, probably the best player in the world.

Before the opening game Valeri outlined his plans to Roger Milla. He saw the veteran player as Cameroon's secret weapon. "We need to save your energy till the right moment," he said. "So I'll name you as a substitute to start the game. When the time comes, I'll bring you on. Then you can use your speed and power."

Milla only played the last eight minutes of the opening game against Argentina, but it didn't matter. He watched as his team-mates produced the shock of the tournament. No one expected the under-dogs of world football to challenge the World Cup holders, but that is exactly what happened. For 62 minutes Cameroon tackled hard and matched Argentina stride for stride. Then one of their defenders, Kana Biyik, was sent off for a harsh tackle. Down to ten men, it seemed Cameroon's chance had gone. But five minutes later Omam Biyik rose to head the ball goalwards. The Argentine goalkeeper reacted too late and watched in horror as the ball crept into the net.

Despite having a second player sent off, nine-man Cameroon hung on to beat the

World Cup holders 1-0. The result sent shock waves throughout the football world. The stage was now set for Roger Milla to make his dramatic impact on the tournament.

Cameroon's next match was against Rumania, a strong and skilful side. Milla was again named among the substitutes. With an hour of the match played, the game seemed to be heading for a dull goalless draw. Then, as the hot sun went down in the Italian sky, a ripple of anticipation went through the Cameroon supporters. Here

was the moment they'd been waiting for. The small, stocky figure of Roger Milla stood up and stripped off his tracksuit top. The coach had decided the time to play his secret weapon had arrived.

Only fourteen minutes of the game were left when Milla challenged a defender outside the penalty area. The ball broke loose and the oldest player on the pitch was the quickest to react. Milla raced after the ball like a greyhound and struck his shot sweetly into the net. As the goalkeeper picked the ball out, Milla ran to the corner flag and performed a bottom-wiggling dance of delight in front of the Cameroon supporters.

Milla wasn't finished, either. Ten minutes later Rumania gave the ball away again. This time Milla shuffled wide and unleashed a thunderbolt shot that the goalkeeper hardly saw. There was no need for dancing.

He sank to his knees in sheer happiness. The coach's plan had worked and Cameroon's super-sub had won the game. At 38, Roger Milla entered the history books as the oldest player ever to score in a World Cup. Cameroon had made history too, as only the second African nation to get past the first round of the tournament.

In the next round Cameroon were drawn to play Colombia. It was a classic meeting of two opposite styles – the cunning fox against the roaring lion. Colombia played a clever,

38

short-passing game, patiently waiting for the moment to pounce and score. Cameroon, in contrast, were hard-tackling, fast and direct. Both teams had players who'd caught the imagination of the fans. Colombia had the mop-haired Rene Higuita, a goalkeeper who made a habit of wandering outside his area to dribble, pass or even head the ball. Cameroon, of course, had Roger Milla, the aging supersub with the electric burst of speed. It was these two players – Higuita and Milla – who would settle the game in a moment of high drama.

As usual Milla started on the sub's bench. This time the coach waited until shortly after half-time to bring him into the action. Again the score was 0-0, but Colombia should have been ahead. They'd already hit the bar and missed several good chances. The game went into extra time. It needed something special to break the

deadlock. As usual, it was Milla who provided it. Taking a clever pass, he raced past one defender, hurdled the tackle of a second, and crashed the ball home with his powerful left foot.

It was a dazzling goal. Yet Milla was saving the finale till last. Two minutes later Higuita, Colombia's crazy goalkeeper, set off on one of his ventures upfield. Forty yards out of his goal he tried one trick too many. He took a pass from a defender and tried to beat a Cameroon player. Unfortunately for him that player was Roger Milla.

The alert striker saw his chance and bore down on the goalkeeper. In a split second he'd tackled Higuita and stolen the ball. He romped away to plant it in the back of the unguarded net. Cameroon and Milla had done it again. They were through to the quarter-finals!

After the game Higuita was brave enough to admit his error. "No question about it," he said. "It was a mistake. It was as big as a house." Milla meanwhile had become a national hero in Cameroon. In the capital, Yaounde, people danced in the street, waving life-size pictures of the legendary striker.

Requests poured in to put a statue of "the old lion" in the city square. Cameroon's Russian coach was full of praise for the man he'd called into his squad at the last minute.

"He enlivens the game. Every time he comes on, he enthuses the players around him."

TV companies across the globe queued up to interview Milla. But they found him typically modest about his performance. "All I did was to be in good physical condition and help the national team," he shrugged. "I came on in the second half and was fortunate enough to score two goals. I am happy for myself and for my companions."

For an African nation to reach the World Cup quarter-finals was a fairy tale come true. They carried the banner of all underdogs before them.

When the World Cup started few had expected Cameroon to win a match. Now they found themselves only two games away from the final. Could they go any further? Could Milla, the man with rockets in his boots, do it a third time?

Two things stood in their way. One was the loss of four key players. At times the Lions of Africa had roared too ferociously for their own good. They'd picked up 11 yellow cards for fouls in the tournament. That meant four of their team had to miss the quarter-final. The other obstacle in their path was England. With players like Paul Gascoigne and Gary Lineker in their side, England were expected to put Cameroon firmly in their place.

It didn't turn out that way. In the most dramatic game of the tournament, Milla and Cameroon gave England the fright of their lives.

Milla again started on the sub's bench. "I am a reserve officer, a little old man who can still be of service," he said, smiling.

In the first half England took the lead, but they only kept it thanks to their goalkeeper, Peter Shilton, and his string of great saves. 1-0 down at half-time, Cameroon's coach told his super-sub to limber up. If ever his country needed its secret weapon it was now. As in the previous games, Milla's arrival on the pitch seemed to inspire Cameroon. He made his team-mates walk taller and play like heroes. Milla's scorching pace and strength on the ball soon caused panic in England's defence.

Twisting and turning in the penalty box, he was tripped by Gascoigne. Penalty to Cameroon! Kunde, the centre-back, took it and scored.

England 1 – Cameroon 1.

Three minutes later Cameroon were in the lead. Milla spotted his fellow sub, Ekeke, making a run and put him through to score. In half an hour Milla had turned the game on its head. Cameroon held on until they were only eight minutes away from the World Cup semi-final. But again their hot-headed tackles cost them dear. Lineker was fouled and scored from the penalty spot. *Cameroon 2 – England 2.*

The game went to extra-time. In a nail-biting finish both sides had chances, but Cameroon gave away a second penalty. Lineker picked himself up and calmly scored again. At the final whistle England's players looked exhausted and mighty relieved.

Cameroon's fairy tale had finally come to an end, but not before they'd given the world some football to remember. Germany won the World Cup that year but it was the Lions of Africa who stole the glory. Above all, one "little old man" who came out of retirement at the last minute won the hearts of fans from Milan to Mexico City. As one sportswriter wrote, "Cameroon were the team of the tournament and Milla was its heart, soul, mascot and cutting edge. They provided the world with all the things we look for in sport – excitement, joy . . . and above all, hope."

Back on the little island of Réunion, the players of St Pierre cheered every one of Cameroon's games on television. As Milla poached the ball from the Colombian keeper to score, young Emile remembered the words his hero had spoken that day: "Never, never stop playing . . . you never know when your chance will come."

Did you know...?

Great Goalscorers

1. Bobby Charlton was England's greatest ever goalscorer, with 49 goals between 1958 and 1970. Gary Lineker was just one goal short of equalling Charlton's record when he ended his England career in 1993.

2. The greatest ever goalscorer in football history was the Brazilian wizard, Pelé, who scored 1,281 goals in 1,363 professional games. In 1959 alone he scored 126 goals. When he scored his 1,000th goal in 1969, he dedicated it to "the poor little children of Brazil."

3. Sometimes a goal opportunity is simply too good to miss. When Brazilian striker Roberto Rivelino was playing for Corinthians he saw that the opposition's goalkeeper was still saying his prayers after the whistle blew for kick-off! He just kicked the ball straight into the net over the goalie's head!

4. Michel Platini of France scored in every single game of the 1984 European Championships, including two hat-tricks. In the final France beat Spain 2-0 with Platini on the score-sheet as usual.

5. Some strikers are so good they can even score goals in their sleep! In an England v

Austria match, Nat Lofthouse crashed into the Austrian goalkeeper as he went to kick the ball. He knocked himself unconscious, but the ball still went in!

6. Some famous goalscorers have only scored one goal in their playing history – but that's not bad if you're a goalkeeper! In 1999 Carlisle United were dramatically saved from relegation out of the football league when their goalkeeper scored following a corner in the fourth minute of injury time.

Pelé, King of the Street

Bauru, Brazil, 1946

Dondhino was hunting under the bed.

"Celeste!" he shouted. "Have you seen my sock?"

"Which sock?" his wife called back.

"My football sock. The yellow one."

"You should take care of them," Celeste scolded him. "We haven't got the money to go spending on new socks."

"But I need it!" Dondhino pleaded. "I've

got to go training this morning. I can't play in my bare feet!"

Celeste shrugged her shoulders. If it was anything to do with football, she wasn't interested. Dondhino played for Bauru Athletic – a professional club in Brazil. But football hadn't made him rich. Like many Brazilians, his family had barely enough food to eat. Their house was a small shack on Rubens Arruda Street with a roof that let in the rain.

Dondhino ran out of the door carrying his bag. Outside he passed his young son,

Edson, playing football with his friends in the street. The boys were playing with a small, yellow ball. Edson flicked it up skilfully and caught it on his thigh. Just as he did, the "ball" started to unravel.

"My sock!" yelled Dondhino. "I've been looking for that everywhere!"

He grabbed the dusty sock and emptied out the rags Edson had stuffed it with.

"But Dad!" protested little Edson. "That's our ball!"

Dondhino had no time for arguments. "I've told you a hundred times, Edson. You are not to borrow my socks for playing football. Now go inside."

Edson hung his head. The other boys slunk away to find something else to play with. No one in Rubens Arruda Street owned a proper football. Footballs cost money and no one had any to spare. The children's street games were played with stones or rolled-up socks.

Inside the house, Edson had to face another lecture from his Mum. She folded her arms and frowned at him .

"How many times have I told you not to play football in the street?"

"But, Mum, all my friends play!"

"Football is a waste

of time, Edson."

Edson looked away. "Dad is a footballer," he said quietly.

"And you're not going to waste your life like him. Forget football. Footballers get injured."

Edson sighed. His mum always said the same thing. "Footballers get injured." It was because of his dad's accident. One day Dondhino had been brought home from the hospital after a match. His leg had been broken in a bad tackle. He missed the rest of the season, hobbling around on crutches. Celeste said nothing but her eyes followed her husband accusingly. While Dondhino was injured the family had no wages coming in to pay the bills.

Even when Dondhino got back to playing his leg was never the same again. Celeste never went to watch her husband's matches. She dreaded him breaking his leg again. Even more, she dreaded her son following in his father's footsteps. Every night she whispered the same prayer in the dark: "Please God, don't let my boy grow up to be a footballer. Let him be something else, dear God."

Edson wanted to please his mother but he couldn't help wanting to play football. Already he could dribble round boys twice his age and, like all Brazilians, he dreamed of one day pulling on the bright yellow shirt of his country.

When he was old enough, Edson's mother sent him to school. Not all the boys in his street went. Some of them stayed home and played football on the street all day. *Pelados* they called it – street football. That's how Edson got his nickname – Pelé, king of the pelados. Sometimes boys from his street stopped him on the way to school.

"Hey Pelé! Don't go to school, it's boring. Come and play football with us, Pelé!"

Edson would wheel round and glare at them furiously. "Don't call me that! My name's Edson."

"OK, OK! Come and play football."

But Edson wouldn't. He'd promised his mother he would go to school and learn. She wanted him to be clever when he grew up so that he could find a good job. Maybe he'd grow up to be a teacher or work in a bank, she said. Then one day they'd move to a proper house. He wouldn't have to share a bed with his brothers and the roof wouldn't let in the rain at nights. Edson wanted his mother to have a big white house like the ones he'd seen in the rich quarter. He tried to work hard at school, but as soon as he got home he ran outside to play football with his friends.

One day the boys on the street had the idea of starting their own football club. For days they argued over different names. Someone suggested Rubens Arruda Street Boys' Football Club. But it was too long and clumsy. Then one day they saw a street in Bauru called 7th September. It sounded right – the 7th September Club.

Choosing a name was the easy part, but a football club needed shirts and boots and the 7th September club didn't even have a ball to play with. Edson and his friends started to try and raise money. Sometimes they stood on street corners selling football cards or cigarettes. Between them they earned a few coins – but it was never enough.

One day Edson and an older boy, Paulo, saw a lorry parked in front of a store. The driver had gone for his coffee break, leaving his cargo unguarded. One of the sacks on the back of the lorry had a split in the corner.

Paulo pointed at them. "Look, Pelé. There's peanuts in those sacks."

Edson knew what he was thinking. "No, Paulo. What if we get caught?"

"We won't," said Paulo breezily. "We'll just take a few handfuls. Who's going to know?"

He strolled casually up to the lorry. "Come on!" he hissed.

Edson hesitated. Paulo was already dragging one of the sacks off the lorry. He showed Edson a handful of brown peanuts.

"Think of how much money we can make selling these."

Soon Edson was dipping his own hands into the sack and filling his pockets.

Just then they heard voices. The driver was coming back from his break.

"Run Pelé, run!" cried Paulo. The two boys took to their heels, scattering a trail of peanuts behind them. The driver gave chase but they soon lost him on the crowded street.

Edson never told his mother about the stolen peanuts. He knew she'd be ashamed that her son was a thief. Stealing the peanuts hadn't even been worth it. When they counted their earnings, they still hadn't made enough money to buy one pair of football boots. The 7th September team had to play in their socks.

By the time Edson was ten, the club had a new name. They were called Americana. With the new name they'd also gained a coach. Ze Leite had watched the boys play and thought they had great potential. He had big plans for his new team. "I'm going to enter you in the Avelone Junior Cup," he announced one day. Edson's face lit up. All the top boys' sides in Bauru played in the Avelone Cup. But how could they hope to compete?

"We still haven't got any boots," he grumbled. "We won't stand a chance if we're the only team playing in our socks."

"I've already thought of that," smiled Ze Leite. He went to fetch a large bag and emptied it out in front of them. Edson and the others stared in amazement. At their feet lay a large pile of football boots. At least a dozen pairs.

"What did you do, steal them?" asked Paulo.

Ze Leite shook his head, grinning hugely. He explained how he'd gone to one of the local professional football clubs, Noroeste. The manager hadn't wanted to listen at first but Ze Leite wouldn't go away. He kept telling him that his street boys were the future of Brazil. In the end he came away with a bag of old boots that the club no longer needed.

Kitted out in their second-hand boots, Americana entered the Avelon Junior Cup. With Edson in the team they were unstoppable. The final was played in the Bauru Athletic Stadium and 5,000 people turned up to see them play. Edson scored the goals which won the cup that day. He heard people in the crowd calling, "Pelé! Pelé!" The nickname had stuck with him and now he began to accept it. He was Pelé, King of the Street.

Soon after, he was asked to join

Bauru Athletic's boys' team. His father was proud to have his son playing for his own club. But his mother didn't congratulate him. She turned her face away and went back to her sewing.

Bauru's team coach was Valdermar de Brito, a footballer who had once worn the yellow shirt of Brazil. One morning, when Pelé was fifteen, Valdermar came to Edson's house with wonderful news.

"Dondhino. I'm going to Sao Paulo soon and I'd like to take Pelé with me. They want him to play at Santos."

Santos! They were one of the most famous clubs in all of Brazil. Pelé could see his father was as thrilled as he was. But what would his mother say? Just then she appeared at the door, wiping her hands on a cloth. Her face had a determined look Pelé knew well.

"He's not going, Valdermar. He's

only a boy. He's staying here with his mother and father."

"But Celeste," Valdermar argued, "he could become famous with Santos and earn a lot of money. I think Pelé has the talent to become a great footballer."

Celeste shook her head. "He's not going to be a footballer. Footballers always get injured. Goodbye Valdermar."

For the rest of the day, Pelé slouched around the house with his hands in his pockets. The chance of a lifetime was waiting for him in Sao Paulo, but he knew his mother would never agree to let him go.

To his surprise Valdermar came back to the house that evening. He wasn't giving up. For a long time his parents sat at the table with Valdermar, talking in low voices. Edson sat by the front door listening. He knew his whole future depended on the outcome of the conversation. At last his mother came and crouched down beside him. She put a hand to his cheek and looked at him sadly.

"They want to take you away from me, Edson. They say you're a man, now. Go, then. Go to Santos. Be a footballer if that's what you really want."

Edson went to Santos. At first he played

badly because he was homesick and missed his family. Every day he expected the coach to call him over and send him home to Bauru. But gradually his thin legs got stronger and he started to show the talent that Valdermar had predicted. At the age of 16 he was playing in Santos' first team and a year later he'd achieved his dream of pulling on the yellow shirt of Brazil.

In 1958 the World Cup was held in Sweden and Pelé was selected in the Brazilian squad. People said that at 17 he was too young, Brazil were playing kids in their side. But by the time Brazil reached the final against Sweden, Pelé was the name on everyone's lips. In the semi-final he had scored a hat-trick and followed it up with two more glorious strikes in the final, as Brazil's dazzling skills took them to a 5-1 win. Soon people were saying that

Pelé was not only the best player Brazil had ever seen, he was going to be the greatest footballer of all time.

When the Brazilian team arrived home a week later, Pelé's parents were among the big crowd at the airport. As Pelé emerged from the aeroplane and waved, a huge cheer went up. Dondhino looked at his wife.

"What do you think now, Celeste? Is our son a footballer?"

Celeste smiled back at him. "Yes, Dondhino. He's a great footballer – just like his father."

Did you know…?

Footballing heroes

1. Pelé is without doubt the greatest footballing hero of all time. His breathtaking skills helped Brazil to win the World Cup three times – in 1958, 1962 and 1970. He was declared an "official national treasure" by the Brazilian government in 1958, and he now works for them as Minister for Sport.

2. Even 25 years after retiring, Bobby Charlton is still a hero for people around the world, and is England's highest ever goalscorer. His trademark was a scorching

shot with either foot from outside the penalty area. He won 106 caps for England.

3. Despite being one of the most talented footballers of all time, Argentinian Diego Maradona is remembered more for one goal against England than for his skill. In the quarter-final of the 1986 World Cup he fisted a ball into the goal, and amazingly it was allowed. He said afterwards that it was partly due to the "hand of God", and it has become one of the best known moments in the history of football.

4. George Best won 37 caps for Northern Ireland and helped Manchester United to win the European Cup for the first time

with his dazzling ball skills. In 1968 he won the Footballer of the Year award and the European Player of the Year trophy.

5. Franz Beckenbauer is the only man to lead his team to victory in the World Cup both as a player and as a manager. He was the captain of the German team when they won the trophy in 1974, and their manager when they lifted it again in 1990.

Pickles Saves the World Cup

London, 1966

Among the great heroes of World Cup
history, one name is often forgotten. That
name is Pickles. Pickles was small for a
hero – standing next to today's players he
would hardly come up to their knees. His
face was white except for two black patches
over his eyes. And he could do a curious
trick with his ears which stood to attention
when his master whistled. In most heroes

this might have looked odd, but Pickles was a dog. Small as he was, it was thanks to him that England lifted the famous Jules Rimet World Cup trophy at Wembley on 30 July 1966.

Pickles' story begins on 21 March of that famous year. As usual he was having his breakfast from his bowl while his master, Dave, read the paper. Suddenly Dave let out a cry of surprise.

"Get away!"

Pickles pricked up his ears. Maybe it was time for his morning walk.

"What's that then, love?" asked Dave's wife Jean, helping herself to more jam.

"Somebody's only gone and pinched the World Cup!" said Dave.

"They never have!"

"It says so here." Dave read out the article.

"Thieves stole the World Cup from an exhibition at Westminster Hall yesterday. The solid gold trophy – worth £30,000 – was taken from an upstairs room right under the noses of security guards. Police are looking for a man in his late thirties, with greasy black hair, thin lips and possibly a scar on his face."

"Ha ha!" giggled Jean. "Sounds like a proper villain."

Dave gave a low whistle. Pickles' ears

stood to attention, but Dave went on talking. "And listen to this: there's a reward of £6,000 for anyone who helps the police to find the trophy. Six thousand quid. Think what you could do with that, Jean!"

Jean thought. "We could buy a car," she said.

"And a colour TV," added Dave.

"Go to Spain for our holiday. Think of that," said Jean longingly.

It was a dream, of course. Six thousand pounds was more than Dave earned in a whole year.

 Pickles, meanwhile, had come closer to the table. Money didn't really interest him. Right now he had his eye on a piece of greasy bacon rind on the edge of his master's plate. He kept quite

still until Dave looked his way. Then he gave his "sad hungry dog" look.

"All right Pickles, you old scrounger," Dave laughed. He dropped the stringy bacon into Pickles' waiting mouth. "Come on then, boy. Time for our walk, eh?"

Dave Corbett lived in Norwood. He was a lighterman on the River Thames in London. His job was to light the old-fashioned gas-lamps along the river. It wasn't a well paid job but Dave thought it had its good points. He liked walking by the Thames in the evening when the city was quieter. Sometimes Pickles trotted beside him and waited patiently at each lamp.

When all the lamps were lit, Dave sat on a bench to admire the scene. The reflected street lights danced like fireflies on the black river. "Look at that, Pickles. That's a picture, that is," said Dave.

Pickles knew nothing about the stolen World Cup. Or about the part he was to play in its recovery. In another part of London the story was unfolding. A brown paper package lay open on a desk. It was

addressed to Joe Mears, Chairman of the Football Association. Joe Mears stared at it. He was a man who often received important packages, but he'd never got anything like this before. Inside the brown paper was a piece of metal, no bigger than the palm of his hand. It had eight sides and shone with the brilliance of gold. There was a short note scrawled on a piece of paper:

> This is the top of the World Cup. If you want the rest of it back it will cost you £15,000. Wait for instructions and don't talk to anybody!

Joe Mears was ready to believe this was part of the missing World Cup. The question was, what should he do about it? If he obeyed the note he was bargaining with a criminal. But if he phoned the police...

Just then the phone rang. He picked up the receiver.

"Did you get it?" a man's voice demanded roughly.

"Who is this?" asked Joe.

"That's my business. Did you get it? The package I sent you."

"Yes, I got it. Where's the rest of it?"

"You'll see it, if you do what I say. Ever read the evening papers?"

Joe was confused by the question. "Of course, what's that got to do with it?"

"I want you to put an advert in the paper. The *Evening Standard*. When I see it I'll know you've got the money."

"What sort of advert?" asked Joe.

"Just say, 'Willing to do business – Joe.' Then I'll know we've got a deal."

"£15,000 is a lot of money," objected Joe.

"You'll find it. Then we'll talk again."

The mysterious caller put the phone down. Joe rested his chin in his hands. For a long time he sat like that, thinking. Then he picked up the phone and dialled a number.

"Hello, I'd like to speak to Scotland Yard, please. It's urgent."

A few days later Dave Corbett was reading his morning paper again. Pickles was nosing under the breakfast table. He'd spied a cornflake that had been lying in a corner. The cornflake was two weeks old and covered in fluff but Pickles wasn't a fussy eater. Up above the table he could hear his master and mistress talking.

"That was quick. They've caught him," said Dave's voice.

"Who's that, love?" asked Jean, absently.

"The thief that pinched the World Cup. Police got a tip-off from some bloke and picked him up. And I'll tell you what else."

"What?"

"He came from round here."

"Never! The thief did?"

"Yeah. It says here: 'Edward Bletchley, a dock worker from south east London.'"

"Just think," laughed Jean. "We could have been living next door to him all the time." Dave laughed too.

Jean asked, "Did they get the cup back?"

"Nope," said Dave. "Doesn't sound like it. They're still looking. Maybe the thief won't tell them where it is."

"That's evidence," said Jean wisely. "If they haven't got no evidence, they can't put him away."

Pickles had finished the cornflake and wandered off into the hall. He fetched his lead and brought it into the kitchen. Going over to Dave, he dropped it at his feet. Dave looked at the lead.

"What's this then, keeping you waiting am I?"

Pickles gave him a forlorn look.

"All right, all right, just let me finish my tea and we'll go."

Five minutes later Pickles and Dave were out for their morning stroll. Dave kept him on the lead for the first part, until they'd crossed the busy main road. Then they walked down the avenue on their way to the park. It was quieter here, so Dave bent down and let Pickles off the lead.

The avenue was a wide road lined with elm trees. On one side there was a line of rambling, three-storey, Edwardian houses.

Once they'd been elegant but now they were shabby and run-down. In the gardens rose bushes fought a losing battle with nettles and weeds. Pickles liked this road. He kept his eyes skinned for any cats lurking in the garden wilderness. Once he'd chased a big ginger tom off a wall and it had hissed at him from under a gate.

He padded ahead of Dave and stopped by a house with a wide driveway. This was a likely garden to go cat-hunting. There was a dark jungle of bushes to the right of the gate. Pickles caught sight of something white under some leaves. He stalked towards it cautiously. You never knew when a scratching, hissing ball of fur might jump out at you.

"Pickles! Come outta there!" Dave called from outside the gate.

Pickles pretended not to hear. He sniffed at the white thing. It wasn't a cat, it was something rolled up in newspaper. Maybe there was a large juicy bone inside. He got hold of the paper with his teeth and pulled. Just when he'd got it out from under the bush, Dave came up behind him.

"This is someone's garden, mate. You'll get us in trouble. What you got, there?"

Dave pulled the bundle of newspaper away, ignoring Pickles' whines of protest.

There was something inside. Checking to see if anyone was watching, he unrolled it. Wrapped inside were two more pieces of paper. He unfolded the first. It contained a heavy blue object. Dave read the words "Brazil 1962" on it. He couldn't make much of that so he unwrapped the second piece. Pickles moved nearer to sniff at it.

There was a statue in the paper. It was not much bigger than a milk bottle and was in the shape of an angelic figure holding up a small eight-sided bowl. When Dave rubbed the dust with his sleeve the metal shone like real gold.

"Blimey!" said Dave. He gave a long, low whistle. Pickles crouched low, hoping they were going to play a game of fetch. But Dave put out a hand and fondled his head.

"Know what, my old mate?" he said. "I think you might've found what they're all looking for."

The next few days were a whirlwind. First there was the question of the £6,000 reward. It was offered by the insurance firm who stood to pay out if the cup wasn't found. With the reward

Jean wanted to book a holiday in Spain. Dave wanted a new TV first so he could watch England play in the World Cup. But when the two of them arrived at the offices of the insurance company, they got a nasty shock. Someone else had already been to claim the reward. The rival was Mr Joe Mears who had helped the police to arrest the thief.

"But that's not fair!" Jean protested. "We found the cup. Not him!"

"That's right," agreed Dave. "It was my dog Pickles who found it. If it wasn't for him you'd still be looking."

The insurance firm said they'd need time to consider the two claims. Jean and Dave went away empty-handed and disappointed. Perhaps there wouldn't be any new TV sets or holidays in Spain after all. Perhaps the reward would go to Mr Joe Mears, the chairman of the FA.

"I bet he's not short of a bob or two," said Jean. "It's not fair."

There followed days of waiting. At last a phone call came just as Dave was getting ready to go out to work. He picked up the receiver.

"Yes . . . we will? That's fantastic news. Thank you!"

He called for Jean. When she came in he was dancing round the room as if he'd just scored the winning goal at Wembley. "What?" she said. "Tell me what?"

"The £6,000 reward is ours, that's what!" said Dave.

That was just the

start. Soon there were more letters and telephone calls. The papers all wanted a photo of the dog who'd found the World Cup. Pickles was awarded a medal from the Canine Defence League and a year's supply of meaty chunks from a dog-food company. The same week Dave and Jean were guests of honour at the Café Royal in London. There they were given a cheque for £1,000 – the first part of the reward. Pickles wasn't impressed with the size of the cheque, but his mouth watered when he saw the huge bone that was for him.

"Hurst shoots! It's hit the crossbar and bounced down. England think they've scored but the referee's running across to consult his linesman."

The commentator's voice rose with the tension. Watching on their new TV set,

Dave and Jean were on the edge of their seats. The score was 2-2 in the World Cup final against Germany – with the match deep into extra-time. Would the Swiss referee give the goal? As Dave and Jean held their breath, he pointed to the centre circle. England were ahead!

That was how it stayed 'till a minute from the end. Then, with fans spilling on to the pitch, Geoff Hurst homed in on the German goal again. "*They think it's all over . . .*" said the commentator. "*It is now!*" he shouted, as Hurst's shot bulged in the roof of the net. Dave and Jean hugged each other and whooped with joy.

Soon after, England's captain, Bobby Moore, went up to receive the little gold trophy from the Queen. Dave pointed excitedly.

"There it is! Look, Pickles! It's the World Cup, come and see!"

But the hero of the hour was in the kitchen, missing all the excitement. Winning a World Cup was all very well, but a year's supply of dog food – that was not to be sniffed at.

Did you know...?

World Cup Wonders

1. Pickles wasn't the only dog to find fame during the World Cup. In the 1962 tournament a dog ran on to the pitch during the quarter-final between England and Brazil and was picked up by England forward Jimmy Greaves. The dog was later named after the Brazilian star Garrincha.

2. The first ever World Cup tournament was held in Uruguay in 1930, and the hosts beat Argentina 4-2 in the final. The two countries were such fierce enemies that the teams were guarded by armed soldiers and

the fans were searched for guns before the match.

3. The first penalty shoot-out was introduced in the 1982 World Cup. England have been knocked out of the tournament twice on penalties - in the 1990 semi-final and the 1998 second round.

4. One of the highest ever scores in a World Cup qualifying game went to New Zealand, who beat Fiji 13-0 on the way to the 1982 World Cup finals in Spain. The Fiji team had been drinking brandy in their hotel bar, and had to be dragged on to the pitch to play the game!

5. In the 1966 World Cup finals you could buy tickets for ten matches, including the final itself, and it would set you back just £3.87½ pence. In the 1998 World Cup finals in France a pass that got you into only five first-round matches cost between £70 and £100, and black market tickets sold for hundreds more.

6. The World Cup was stolen *again* in 1983 in Rio de Janeiro in Brazil. No Pickles could have found it this time, though – it was melted down by the thieves. The Brazilian Football Association had to ask for an exact replica to be made.

The Hungarian Heroes

Budapest, Hungary, 1953

It was nearly three o'clock in the afternoon. Stefan and Jozef were on their way home from the factory. The tram rattling through the city streets of Budapest was usually crowded at this time. Most people had to stand, hanging on to the hand-straps, packed together as tight as sardines in a tin. But today Stefan and Jozef had seats all to themselves. The tram was almost empty and outside the streets of Budapest looked like a ghost town. Everyone was at home waiting for the match to start.

"You think we'll make it home in time for kick-off?" asked Stefan.

"Of course we'll make it," said Jozef. All the same he looked anxiously out of the window for a clock.

"Everybody else is home by now. It's not fair that all the other factories started work earlier than us," grumbled Stefan.

"We're nearly there. Stop moaning," Jozef told him.

The tram stopped outside an electrical shop where a bald man hurried out the door. On a trolley he was pushing a box-shaped radio the size of a sink. Few Hungarians could afford a TV set in 1953, and so for most people in Budapest radio was the only way of getting news of the game. By now, every radio set had been bought or rented. Jozef pointed to a poster in the café next door. It said, "We are broadcasting the Match of the Century."

"The Match of the Century," purred Stefan. "I wish we could be there to see it. Wouldn't you like to be standing in the famous Wembley Stadium right now?"

Jozef nodded. He tried to imagine the scene. England in white, walking out side by side with the proud Hungarian team in their cherry red shirts. 100,000 fans on their feet, eager to see the Match of the Century.

The game was billed as a friendly but actually it was a show-down between two famous sides. England's proud boast was that they'd never once lost a game on their home turf. Some Englishmen went as far as to say that their team was simply unbeatable at Wembley. But Hungary was their greatest test yet. Not only were the Hungarians the 1952 Olympic Champions, they were also on a run of over 20 games unbeaten themselves. One team's record had to come to an end. Who would win the clash of giants?

Stefan was looking worried again. "The radio said the weather in London was foggy this morning. You don't think they've called it off?"

Jozef shook his head. "They're playing. Look at the streets. They're deserted. Everyone in Budapest is at home glued to their radio sets. We'd have heard if it was off."

"You really think we can beat them?" asked Stefan.

"Of course," said Jozef. "We have Puskas. He's the greatest player in the world!"

"Yes," said Stefan, doubtfully. "But England have some good players too. And no one's ever beaten them at Wembley. No one."

"There has to be a first time," smiled Jozef. He didn't want to listen to Stefan's doubts. Stefan always feared the worst. Privately, Jozef wasn't as confident as he sounded. He knew their Hungarian side was good. But were they good enough to succeed where other great sides had failed? Many teams had gone to Wembley and come away empty-handed.

The tram was slowing again. With a sudden jolt, Jozef realized it was their stop. Stefan was already on his feet and heading towards the door. The tram lurched and he almost fell into the conductor.

They ran through the deserted city streets. Stefan was the first to reach the stairs to their block of flats. Jozef was out of breath by the time he reached his door. He turned the key in the lock and glanced anxiously at the hall clock. Ten past three – only a few minutes to spare. It had been close but they were just in time for kick-off.

When his daughter saw him, however, she shook her head sadly.

"What is it? What's the matter?" asked Jozef in alarm. He pushed his way past into the room, followed by Stefan. The flat was already crowded with friends and neighbours who'd come to listen to the match on Jozef's radio. His eldest son, Victor, was kneeling beside it, his ear pressed against the speaker. He looked up miserably as Jozef came in.

"It's no good, Dad. It's not working. We can't get any sound."

Jozef groaned in disbelief. Stefan rolled his eyes. "I knew it," he said. "I knew we should have gone to the square with everyone else! They've got loudspeakers in the square."

For a few precious minutes Jozef fiddled desperately with the old radio set. Everyone in the room waited in tense silence. Inwardly, Jozef cursed himself for not having rented a new radio weeks before. The Match of the Century was about to begin and his set had to pick today to give up the ghost! Unscrewing the back, he checked to see if any wires were loose. But when he put it back together, there wasn't even a buzz from the speaker. Sweating, Jozef looked at the clock. 3.15. The match was kicking off. There was no time to lose.

"Quick!" he bellowed to the room in general. "Gregor's café. They'll be broadcasting the match there."

The room emptied in seconds. People

grabbed coats and hats as they charged out of the flat like stampeding buffalo. Along the hall, down the stairs and out into the street they ran. Stefan, Jozef, his wife and four children, streamed down the road with a dozen neighbours puffing and wheezing behind them.

Five minutes later Jozef flung the door of the café open. The room was heavy with smoke and packed with bodies. Every table was taken and every ear was listening intently to the voice on the radio. Their party crowded into the café, standing anywhere they could.

"Any score?" Jozef whispered to a woman at the nearest table.

"1-0," she said. Jozef's face fell. Only five minutes into the match and Hungary were already losing!

The woman tugged at his sleeve and whispered, "Hidegkuti took it past three men and scored in the first minute. A beauty!"

Hidegkuti? He was *their* centre forward. Hungary had scored in the very first minute of the match! Jozef whispered the amazing news to Stefan. Then the news was relayed to the others in excited whispers.

But even as they were celebrating, the radio commentator's voice became anxious.

"England have the ball. Johnston comes forward over the halfway line. Hungary have some defending to do here. Johnston passes the ball to Mortenson. Mortenson has it just outside the penalty area. He slips the ball wide to Sewell. Sewell shoots left-footed. It's a goal, a tremendous goal! 1-1. England are back in the match."

There were groans all round the café and people shook their heads.

Stefan nudged Jozef. "I told you. It's not going to be so easy. England aren't going to lie down. We're in for a tough game."

"Don't be so gloomy," argued Jozef. "There's plenty of time yet. The match has only just started."

"Shhh!" hissed the woman at the near table, pointing to the radio. People had turned round and were glaring at them.

What happened in the next twenty minutes was so breathtaking that there was hardly time to talk. They listened, caught in the spell of the dramatic voice on the radio.

"Twenty minutes gone, Puskas going forward."

They could picture the imperious Hungarian captain, striding forward with his big chest puffed out.

"Puskas passes to Czibor who's racing down the left. The ball is threaded through to Kocsis. He flicks it back to Hidegkuti. He shoots. Goal! Hidegkuti gets his second to put Hungary back in front!"

Gregor's café erupted with cheers. Stefan hugged Jozef who shouted in his ear, "I told you! I told you!"

But Hungary were only just getting into their stride. They were passing the ball from player to player with little touches and flicks. Their players were constantly changing position, drawing the confused English defenders all over the Wembley turf. At times it seemed as though Hungary had five men in attack. England's goal, said the commentator, was under siege.

"*The ball is moving smoothly from one Hungarian player to another. England can't get a touch at the moment. It's out to Czibor sprinting down the wing again. Czibor pulls the ball back to Puskas. Puskas juggles his way through ... and shoots. What a goal! He smashed that inside the near post. Even the English fans are*

on their feet applauding the Hungarians. Surely that's one of the best goals Wembley's ever seen!"

In the café people were standing up and banging on the tables. Stefan lifted Peter, Jozef's youngest son, into the air. It was unbelievable but minutes later Puskas had done it again.

"Bozsik takes the free kick. The goalkeeper dives. Puskas – it's four! The ball has struck Puskas' heel and flown into the goal. Who would have believed this? Hungary are leading England by four goals to one after only thirty minutes of play!"

The commentator was so excited he was bellowing into his microphone.

By half-time England had managed to pull one goal back, but it didn't dampen anyone's spirits. Jozef and Stefan bought drinks for everyone in their party. Jozef told everyone who would listen that he'd said all along that Hungary would win. Stefan claimed he'd never doubted it – even though it wasn't strictly true. Wiser heads cautioned that the game wasn't over yet. England were only two goals behind, one more and they would be back in the game. Hungary would have to keep up the pressure in the second half.

But Puskas and his team had no intention of relaxing. Ten minutes after the interval the radio commentator's voice rose in excitement.

"Hungary are on the attack again. The ball is crossed towards Czibor. He heads – a brilliant

save by Merrick turning it on to the post. But England aren't out of danger yet. The ball's passed back to Bozsik . . . edge of the penalty area . . . he shoots. Another goal! Hungary's fifth from a thundering drive by Bozsik. The England defenders are shaking their heads. They must wish the game was over . . . "

A few minutes later Hidegkuti got his hat-trick, volleying home his third as Puskas lobbed the ball to him. The game finished Hungary 6 – England 2. Hungary hadn't just broken England's proud home record, they'd given their hosts a lesson in football. At the final whistle English fans were in a state of shock. It wasn't just that their side had been beaten, they had been run ragged. The Hungarians were fitter, faster and played with bewildering skill. Those who were at Wembley that day knew they had glimpsed the football of the future. The Mighty

Magyars (as the British papers called them) had shown they were the soccer masters of the world.

Back in Budapest the little café was noisier than Wembley itself. Everyone went round hugging and kissing each other. Even complete strangers were in each other's arms. Tears were streaming down Stefan's face. Jozef kissed all his children in turn and told them never to forget this day. Old Gregor, who owned the café, ordered free drinks for everyone (which had never been known before!). The wild celebrations went on late into the evening.

All over Budapest the story was the same. In the streets they told how the Hungarian team sat in their dressing room long after the match, singing song after song.

People told the story of the match over and over again to each other. They'd listened to it in their homes, in cafés, shops and department stores, in the city squares and in any place a radio could be found.

Those who had to work found other ways of following the game. In the mines the score was chalked on the sides of the cages lowered into the pits so that the miners could keep up to date with their team's progress.

Afterwards factory workers, students and teachers alike sat down to write telegrams of congratulation to the team. No less than 8,000 telegrams from Hungary were received in London that night! One of them was from Stefan, Jozef and their friends. It read simply: "If football's played for another century, there'll never be another match like this one. We are proud of our Hungarian heroes."

Did you know…?

Record Breakers

1. Brazil are the most successful national team of all time and have lifted the World Cup four times. In 1970 they were even allowed to keep the trophy for ever, and another one was made. But winning the trophy in 1958 and 1962 wasn't enough for their trainer, Americo – after both finals he ran on to the pitch and stole the ball from the referee as a souvenir!

2. In 1999 Manchester United became the first English Club ever to win the "treble" of the FA Cup, the Premier

League and the European Champions' Cup. Manager Alex Ferguson was knighted soon after. He has led his team to 12 major trophies in 13 years, including two "doubles" (Premiership and FA Cup) in 1994 and 1996.

3. Germany have the best overall record in the World Cup: they've lost in the semifinal three times, lost in the final three times, and have won the trophy three times (in 1954, 1974 and 1990). They have also qualified for every finals competition that they have entered.

4. Glasgow Rangers are the most successful Scottish team of all time, having won the Scottish League 48 times between

1891 and 1998. In the 1898/99 season they achieved a world record which has never been beaten, winning every single one of their league matches.

5. The longest single game in football history lasted an incredible 500 minutes. The match, which was between Stockport and Doncaster in March 1946, was finally stopped with a score of only 2-2.

6. The best ball juggler in the world is Ukranian, Nikolai Kutsenko. He juggled a ball for 42 and a half hours non-stop using his feet, legs and head, without the ball ever touching the ground.

Football Crazy Mum

Ashington, Northumberland, 1945

It was a warm summer's evening on
Beatrice Street. Behind the blackened rows
of terraced houses a gang of a dozen boys
were playing football. There was no grass,
the pitch was the street and the goals were
chalked on the red brick walls. The fraying
tennis ball rebounded against them with an
echoing thump.

"Our Jack! Pass! Pass!" called the smallest

boy. He was younger than the others
and had a high, piping voice. But
his tall, older brother gave him the
ball nevertheless.

"Run it, Bob," Jack urged. Bob ran it.
Straight at the four other bigger lads
playing on the other side. He shaped for a
pass to his brother, then swerved the other
way and cut inside two players. The other
boys tried to catch him but he was too fast
for them. His right foot swung and the
tennis ball flew like a missile before
thudding into the goal.

"Great goal, Bob! 14–10 to us." Jack shouted.

"It never is. It's 13–10," argued Billy, the red-haired captain of the other side.

"Fourteen," said Jack flatly, squaring up to him.

"Now lads, no squabbles please," said a firm voice from behind them. Jack and  Bob turned to see their mum watching them. She took off her cardigan and folded it neatly. "So. Whose side am I playing on tonight?"

"Ours, Mum!" said Jack and Bob quickly. They always wanted her on their side. It wasn't just because she was their mum, she was as good

 a footballer as any of the boys on the street.

"That's not fair! You're winning. We want Mrs Charlton," whined Billy.

A few minutes later the game was in full flow again. Mrs Charlton was playing against her two sons. She was still wearing her kitchen apron but she didn't shirk any tackles. As they played she issued instructions to her team, "Pass back, Billy. Now move. Find some space, lad."

Anyone in the village of Ashington would tell you, Cissie Charlton had been playing football since the day she could walk.

Football was in Cissie's blood. In a mining village like Ashington there were only two choices after leaving school. Either you went down the mines or – if you were lucky – you played professional football. Cissie's family had been lucky. Four of her brothers played football for their living. The Milburn boys – Jackie, Jimmy, George and Stan – were well-known in the north-east. All of them were full-backs – fast runners and hard tacklers.

But the most famous member of the family was Cissie's cousin. Jackie Milburn was a centre forward whose goals had won the FA Cup for Newcastle and made him a local legend. When little Jack and Bob went to visit him, they often begged "Uncle

Jackie" to show them the caps he'd won playing for England. The boys would reach out to touch them as if they were spun from pure gold.

From the top of the main street in Ashington you could see the pit-heads of five or six coal-mines. Down below, men worked in the narrow tunnels, bent over 12 hours a day, digging the black coal.

Cissie's husband, Bob, was one of them. When his shift was finished on Friday night or Saturday morning he would head for his mother's house. There he would take his weekly bath, turning the tub water black. The Charlton's house didn't have a bath. There was no heating except the coal fire in the living-room which also served as Cissie's oven.

Cissie had four sons altogether. Jack and Bobby were the first pair and Gordon and Tommy followed after a gap of several years. Cissie didn't want any of her sons following their dad down the mines. It was back-breaking work and pit accidents had claimed many lives. If her boys had any talent she'd rather they became footballers like her brothers.

She'd started taking them to watch Ashington's home games when Bobby was still a baby. Jack would sit with her while Bobby stayed in his pram behind the dressing room. Every time the crowd cheered a goal the baby would jump at the noise.

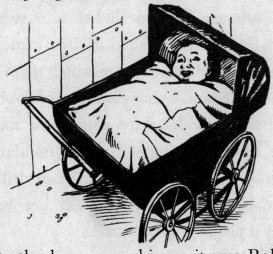

As the boys grew bigger it was Bobby who caught the eye. Jack was bigger and a dogged tackler, but Bobby was blessed with natural talent. Even at the age of nine he had a body swerve and a shot that scorched the grass. When the boys lined up in the park to pick teams, it was always Bobby who was chosen before his older brother. Jack had to put up with the jokes from his pals, but he wasn't the type to be jealous.

He could see his little brother was something special, and he was proud of him.

Cissie encouraged all her four sons to play football. She joined in their games on the street and later went to watch them play for local teams. Other parents used to shout and shriek with excitement on the touch-line. But Cissie watched quietly, nodding to herself at a good pass or a clever dribble. Her boys didn't have to tell her when they'd played a good game.

There was never any spare money in the house, but Cissie was determined her boys should have football kit. Since she couldn't afford football socks she took out her needles and knitted them herself. The socks were red and white. Shorts were more of a problem until Cissie

had a brainwave. It was the early
1940s and the Second World War
was raging against Germany. The
Charlton house, like every other
in the village, had the windows draped
with heavy black-out curtains. The idea
was to stop German pilots spotting the
lights below and dropping their bombs on
Ashington. Cissie, however, had thought of
another use for the thick material. From a
large square she cut out two pairs of baggy
black shorts for Jack and Bobby.

Football boots were another matter.
They had to be bought. When Jack was
seven, Cissie promised him his first pair of
boots for Christmas. She kept an eagle eye
on the local paper and one day an advert
caught her eye.

Boy's football boots. Hardly used.
10 shillings.

Ten shillings is only 50 pence today, but in those days it was almost a day's wages. Still, Cissie was determined Jack would have his boots. She gave him a ten shilling note and he set off at a run for the address given in the paper. Jack found the house and was shown inside by a kindly woman.

She put the boots on the table. Jack looked at them and his heart missed a beat. They were Mansfield Hotspurs — the best football boots you could buy at the time. Not only that, they were almost brand new. Jack wanted the boots more than anything in the world — but he knew better than to show it. At seven years old he'd already learned how to strike a bargain. He looked the boots over several times and sighed.

"I can give you seven shillings for them, Missus."

She was taken aback. "Seven? I

wanted ten. It said so in the paper."

"I know. But I can only give you seven."

She pursed her lips. "I don't know. I wasn't expecting to drop the price."

Jack looked unhappy.

"What about eight then?" said the woman doubtfully.

"Done," said Jack quickly and held out his ten shilling note.

He walked home with the Mansfield Hotspurs tucked under his arm, the proudest boy in Ashington. That day Jack took his first step to becoming a footballer. He also earned his mother's admiration when he handed her back two shillings' change.

Bobby meanwhile was beginning to show his startling talent. At school he was quiet and hard-working. Unlike his elder brother, Bobby passed his exams and went on to Bedlington Grammar School. Jack went to watch him play for his new school team one day. The full-sized goals dwarfed the goalkeepers so the teacher had run a piece of string between the posts to act as a makeshift crossbar below the real one. At one point during the game Bobby picked up the ball twenty five yards out from goal. Taking aim, he let fly with one of his trademark "rockets". The ball flew past the goalkeeper so fast that he didn't even move.

The referee blinked for a moment at little Bobby, then gave a goal-kick. As the goal-keeper hadn't moved, he assumed the ball must have gone over the makeshift cross-bar. Jack knew differently. After the match he took the ball and showed that it was too big to have gone between the string cross-bar and the real one. Bobby's aim had been true and deadly.

Not long after, Jack and Bobby started playing football together for Ashington YMCA. It was an under-18s league which meant they were up against boys who were twice their size. Bobby was only 13 and playing against boys four years older. Once their team lost by 18 goals to nil. Another time they managed to scrape a 2-2 draw and talked about the game for weeks!

In his teens, Bobby's talent soon attracted the attention of professional clubs.

Manchester United sent along their scout, Joe Armstrong, to watch Bobby play for East Northumberland schoolboys. It was a cold, grey day with the grass turned silver by frost. Armstrong stood on the touchline, hands in pockets, watching Bobby swerve and dribble round the opposition. A scout from Sunderland was also at the game. At the final whistle Bobby was disappointed when the Sunderland scout went to speak to his side's goalkeeper. But Joe Armstrong had made a bee-line for Cissie Charlton.

"I don't want to butter you up, Missis,"

he said, "but your boy will play for England before he's twenty-one."

It wasn't long before there were 18 scouts knocking on Cissie Charlton's door. Sometimes she would turn round from raking the fire to find another one in her front room. One scout claimed to have £550 in his briefcase. Mrs Charlton could have the money there and then if her son just signed a contract. But Bobby couldn't be bought with promises of cash. He had already decided – Manchester United was the club for him.

One day a letter arrived for Bobby. He read it through and passed it to his mother.

Her eyes shone. "A trial match for England schoolboys. What about that then, our Jack?"

Jack nodded. "He'll be showing off his own England caps next," he said.

Bobby smiled. "I've got to get in the team first."

Cissie talked about it long and hard with Bobby's old PE teacher Mr McGuiness.

"The one thing that worries me  is he's a bit slow off the mark," she said.

Mr McGuiness agreed. "He's got all the ball skills. If we can quicken him up over twenty yards, he's a certainty."

Cissie pondered how to work on Bobby's speed. Her husband wasn't interested in football and none of the men on the street had time to take on the job. So, true to form, Cissie decided to coach Bobby herself.

Over the next week she took her son over the park every evening and marked out the distances. A 20 metre sprint then back again. An 80 metre sprint then back. Under the critical eye of his mother, Bobby ran back and forth.

Whether it helped she never knew, but Bobby made the England schoolboy team. It was the beginning of a famous career. Joe Armstrong's prediction was right – before he was twenty-one Bobby had won his first England cap. It was one of the proudest moments in Cissie's life – but greater things were still to come. In 1966 Jack was called up to join Bobby in the England World Cup squad. The two brothers played in every match and helped England win the trophy for the only time in their history.

Not long after, Ashington threw a celebration dinner to honour the village's most famous sons. Thousands of people lined the streets to see Jack and Bobby drive past in an open-topped Rolls Royce. Cissie's heart swelled with pride as she watched her two sons waving to the cheering crowds. They'd come an awful long way since chasing a tennis ball down Beatrice Street. And who knows if they would have got there without their football-mad mum?

Did you know…?

Football Families

1. Jack and Bobby Charlton were the first brothers to play for England this century, and they also retired on the same day – 28 April, 1973. The only other brothers to play for England since are Manchester United defenders, Gary and Philip Neville.

2. Ray, Danny and Rod Wallace all played for Southampton in the 1989-90 season. This was the first time for 68 years that three brothers had played together in the samc League team.

3. Four pairs of brothers have played in World Cup Finals – the Evaristos (Argentina 1930), the Walters (Germany 1954), the Charltons (England 1966) and the Van der Kerkhofs (Argentina 1978).

4. The shortest family partnership was between Keith and Gavin Peacock at Gillingham. In 1987 manager Keith Peacock bought his son Gavin from Queen's Park Rangers to play for his third division side. Three weeks later Keith got the sack!

5. The Greek side Olympiakos had five brothers called Andrianopoulos in their 1920s team. Imagine having to

commentate on their matches! And what about the fans – would they have sung "There's only five Andrianopouloses"?

6. In 1955 Wales played two pairs of brothers in their international team – John and Mel Charles and Len and Ivor Allchurch. They beat Northern Ireland 3-2 with a John Charles hat-trick.

141

AIRMAIL FROM...

Would you like to read airmail letters from children in other parts of the world?

Airmail From South East Asia – *Ban Pong – where beetles taste great!* Shrimp writes to you from Thailand, about food, festivals, having fun Thai style, and lots more. Meet Frog, her brother (*not* her pet), and her funny Uncle Boon.

Airmail From Africa – *Ngorongoro – where cow poo is lucky!* Meet Christopher, a boy from Tanzania in Africa. He's dying to tell you all about his tribe, his four mums, and his *very* special cows.

AIRMAIL FROM...

Airmail From South America

Amazonia – where tree frogs go moo!
Maria and Leo are twins from
Copacabana in Brazil. They are going on
a brilliant adventure trip to the Amazon
Jungle, and they're writing to tell *you*
all about it.

Airmail From Canada – *Okotoks –
where moose go shopping!* Read Keri's
pen-pal letters from awesome Alberta in
Canada. She'll tell you all about frozen
winters, Inuit Olympics, and how
cows play bingo!

AIRMAIL FROM...

Airmail From India - *Old Delhi - where elephants go to school!* Hari writes to you with all his news from Old Delhi: about his sister's wedding, Indian gods, cricket, and why an elephant is your best friend.

Coming soon:

Airmail From Australia - *Sydney - where biscuits go surfing!* Meet Sharon from Down Under. She's got some ripper letters for you, about her amazing outback adventure, some weird Ozzie creatures and the sensational sights of Sydney.